Freddie's Blanket

By Joanna Johnson
Illustrated by Eric Johnson

SLATE
FALLS
PRESS

Slate Falls Press, LLC
P.O. Box 7062
Loveland, CO 80537
www.slatefallspress.com

Library of Congress Cataloging-in-Publication Data Johnson, Joanna.
Freddie's Blanket / by Joanna Johnson illustrations by Eric Johnson
ISBN 978-0-578-07199-2 ISBN 0-578-07199-1
Library of Congress Control Number: 2010916231
Signature Book Printing, inc.
www.sbpbooks.com

for Sam

When Freddie was a little baby, his mother wrapped him up carefully in his first blanket. As long as she was close by, he would sleep practically anywhere. Sometimes Freddie slept in his cradle.

Sometimes Freddie slept in the buggy.

And sometimes Freddie slept in his baby sling.

As the months passed, he grew bigger, and before too long, Freddie's first blanket was too small.

The buggy was too small.

Even the baby sling was too small.

It was time for Freddie to sleep in a bigger bed. His mother knit him a new blanket that was just the right size for him. His father played a song on the guitar. And they tucked Freddie in.

But later that night, when his mother came to check on him, Freddie's bed was empty! Freddie had curled up under the train table and fallen asleep with his favorite train.

The next night, Freddie's father found him sleeping under the piano.

And the next night, his sister found him sleeping in the bathtub.

Night after night, Freddie's parents took him back to his bed and tucked him in.

Night after night, Freddie found another interesting place to fall asleep. He would sleep practically anywhere.

But finally, one night, after Freddie's mother wrapped him up carefully in his just-the-right-size blanket, held him snugly in the rocking chair, and read him his very favorite story three times...

...he decided that his bed might just be the best place to sleep after all.

the end

knitting patterns

Freddie's Blanket

Size

Toy 12" square

Baby 32" square

Child 40" square

Yarn

Brown Sheep Serendipity Tweed, 60% cotton, 40% wool, 210 yards per 100 grams

Color A Yellow Buttercup, 0.5 [2, 3] skeins

Color B Teal Orchid, 0.25 [1, 2] skeins

Color C Oregano Leaves, 0.25 [1, 2] skeins

alternate colors shown are:

Color A Baby's Breath

Color B Nectarine Blossom

Color C Wild Rose

Needles

Size US 5 and 7 circular needles about 32" long (straight needles or shorter circulars are fine for the toy version)

Gauge

20 sts over 4 inches in stockinette stitch on size US 7 needles

Pattern Notes

This fun colorwork blanket is created using a very simple slip stitch technique and uses only one color of yarn per row, which makes it a great introduction to colorwork for a beginner as well as a fun knit for experienced knitters. You should have enough yarn left over from the Baby or Child blanket to knit the little Toy sized blanket. If you wish to modify the width of the blanket, simply change the number of cast-on stitches by a variable of 8.

Pattern

Using color A and size 5 needles, CO 63 [159, 199] sts.

Knit 6 rows.

Switch to size 7 needles and begin colorwork pattern as follows:

Row 1- with color B: knit 1 row

Row 2- with color B: purl 1 row

Row 3- with color A: k1, * sl1, k1, sl1, k1, sl1, k3 * repeat to last 6 sts, * sl1, k1 * three times

Row 4- with color A: p1, * sl1, p1, sl1, p1, sl1, p3 * repeat to last 6 sts, * sl1, p1 * three times

Row 5- with color C: knit 1 row

Row 6- with color C: purl 1 row

Row 7- repeat row 3

Row 8- repeat row 4

Repeat the 8 row colorwork pattern until the blanket measures 11.5 [31.5, 39.5] inches from cast on edge, or, until it measures ½ inch shorter than desired length, ending on row 2 or 6 of the pattern.

Switching to size 5 needles and color A, knit 6 rows.

BO all sts.

Using size 5 needle, finish side edges as follows:

With color A and beginning at the very edge of the blanket, pick up 3 stitches for every 4 rows along entire side edge. Knit 6 rows. CO all stitches. Repeat for other side edge.

Finishing

Weave in ends, block lightly.

abbreviations

beg	beginning
BO	bind off
CO	cast on
dpn	double-pointed needle
k2tog	knit two together
k	knit
kfb	knit in front and back of stitch
kw	knitwise
m1	make one by knitting into the back of the loop just below the next stitch
p2tog	purl two together
p2tog tbl	purl two together through the back loop
p	purl
patt	pattern
pm	place marker
pfb	purl in front and back of stitch
pw	purlwise
rem	remain
rs	right side
sl	slip
sm	slip marker
ssk	slip, slip, knit
st	stitch
sts	stitches
st st	stockinette stitch
ws	wrong side
wyib	with yarn in back
wyif	with yarn in front
yo	yarn over

Freddie Platypus

Finished Size 13" Tall

Yarn

Brown Sheep Serendipity Tweed, 60% Cotton, 40% Wool, 210 yards per 100 grams

Nebraska Wheat, 1 skein

Oregano Leaves, 1 skein

For Freddie's Coveralls: Colorado Columbine, 1 skein

Needles

For toy: size US 5 double-pointed needles

For toy coveralls: size US 6 and 7 straight or circular needles

Notions

Three 1/2" buttons for Freddie's coveralls

Small scraps of wool felt in dark brown for eyes

Toy stuffing of your choice-- polyfill, roving, or a blend is fine

Two stitch holders

Gauge

22 st over 4 inches in stockinette stitch on size US 5 needles

Pattern Notes

Freddie Platypus is a seamless toy knit in the round from the top down. His coveralls are knit in two pieces and seamed at the sides with a mattress stitch. He is a quick knit and is sure to please any young child. A pattern for his sister May follows. Remember to use caution when knitting for young children by carefully securing buttons so as to avoid a choking hazard.

Pattern

Head:

Using Nebraska Wheat and size 5 dpns, CO 9 sts. Divide evenly on three needles, pm, and join for working in the round, being careful not to twist the stitches.

K 1 rnd.

Next rnd: * M1, k1 * repeat. 18 sts. Knit 1 rnd.

Next rnd: * M1, k2 * repeat. 27 sts. Knit 1 rnd.

Next rnd: * M1, k3 * repeat. 36 sts. Knit 2 rnds.

Next rnd: * M1, k4 * repeat. 45 sts. Knit 2 rnds.

Next rnd: * M1, k5 * repeat. 54 sts. Knit 2 rnds.

Next rnd: * M1, k6 * repeat. 63 sts. Knit 6 rnds.

Create bill opening:

K2, BO 17, k rest of rnd.

K2, CO 17, k rest of rnd. 63 sts.

K 8 rnds.

Shape neck:

Row 1: * K2tog, k1 * repeat across rnd. 42 sts.

Row 2: * k2, k2tog * three times, k2. Repeat twice more across rnd. 33 sts.

Row 3: kfb 33 times. 66 sts.

K 2 rnds.

* K10, kfb * 6 times. 72 sts.

K 6 rnds.

Create armhole:

First Rnd: K 24 (needle 1). K3, BO 8, K13 (needle 2). K13, BO 8, K3 (needle 3).

Next Rnd: K 24 (needle 1). K3, CO 8, K13 (needle 2). K 13, CO 8, K3 (needle 3). 72 sts.

Body:

K 32 rnds.

Create opening for tail:

K40, BO 16, K16.

K24 (needle 1). K16, CO 8 (needle 2). CO 8, k16 (needle 3).

K 5 rnds.

Create leg openings:

K1, BO 8, k6, BO 8, k to end of rnd.

K1, CO 8, k6, CO 8, k to end of rnd.

K 1 rnd.

K24, then, (k2tog) 24 times. 48 sts.

Slip 12 sts from needle 3 to needle 2.

Graft bottom of toy using kitchener st.

Weave in ends, being sure to close opening at the top of the head.

Block lightly.

Bill:

Using Oregano Leaves, pick up a total of 36 sts around bill opening as follows: 18 sts across top of bill opening (needle 1), 9 sts across half of bottom of bill opening (needle 2), and 9 sts across second half of bottom of bill opening (needle 3). 36 sts.

P 4 rnds.

K 8 rnds.

Shape bill:

(K1, ssk, k12, k2tog, k1) twice. 32 sts.

K 1 rnd.

(K1, ssk, k10, k2tog, k1) twice. 28 sts.

(K1, ssk, k8, k2tog, k1) twice. 24 sts.

(K1, ssk, k6, k2tog, k1) twice. 20 sts. Cut yarn, leaving 30" tail.

Sl 5 sts from needle 2 to needle 3, and graft edge of bill using kitchener st, leaving yarn tail uncut. Using the filling of your choice, stuff the toy head, bill, and neck. Using yarn tail, sew a running st (through both layers of knitting and the stuffing) along the ridge of the bill where the purl rows end and the knit rows begin as shown in diagram.

Arms and Legs:

Using Oregano Leaves, pick up a total of 24 sts around the armhole openings as follows:

Pick up 12 sts along top of opening (needle 1), 6 sts along half of bottom opening (needle 2), and 6 sts along second half of bottom opening (needle 3). 24 sts.

K 12 rnds.

P 1 rnd.

(K3, p1, k4, p1, k3) twice.

Repeat this rnd 6 times more.

(K1, m1, k2, p1, k2, m1, k2, p1, k2, m1, k1) twice. 30 sts.

(K4, p1, k5, p1, k4) twice.

Cut yarn leaving 30" tail.

Sl sts from needle 2 to needle 3.

Graft end of limb using kitchener st, leaving yarn tail uncut.

Repeat for other arm and both legs.

Stuff limbs and body through tail opening.

Using yarn tail and yarn needle, sew running sts (through both layers of knitting and the stuffing) in the "ditches" created by the purl sts on the hands and feet as shown in the diagram.

Tail:

Using Nebraska Wheat, pick up 18 sts across top of tail (needle 1), 9 sts across half of bottom of tail (needle 2), and 9 sts across second half of bottom of tail (needle 3). 36 sts.

K 24 rnds.

Shape tail:

(K1, ssk, k12, k2tog, k1) twice. 32 sts.

K 1 rnd.

(K1, ssk, k10, k2tog, k1) twice. 28 sts.

(K1, ssk, k8, k2tog, k1) twice. 24 sts.

(K1, ssk, k6, k2tog, k1) twice. 20 sts.

Cut yarn, leaving 24" tail.

Stuff tail, and make sure the body, head, and limbs are stuffed to your liking; this is your last chance!

Sl 5 sts from needle 2 to needle 3, and graft edge of tail using kitchener st, leaving the yarn tail long.

Using yarn tail, sew running st (through both layers of knitting and the stuffing) where the tail joins the body as shown in diagram.

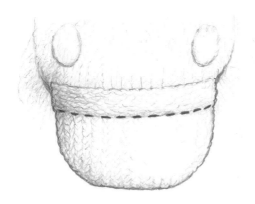

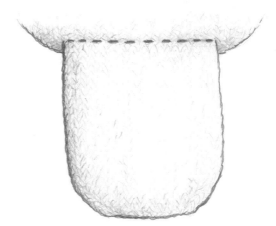

Toy Freddie's Coveralls

Right Front

Using Colorado Columbine and size 6 needles, CO 18 sts.

K 4 rows.

Switch to size 7 needles and knit 1 row, purl 1 row.

Break yarn and sl sts to a holder.

Left Front

Repeat as for right but do not break yarn.

K across left front and across sts from holder. 36 sts.

Work in st st for 4.5 inches, ending on WS row.

K2, ssk, k to last 4 sts, k2tog, k2.

K2, purl to last 2 sts, k2. 34 sts.

Repeat these 2 rows 6 times more. 22 sts.

Make buttonholes

K2, ssk, yo, k2tog, k to last 6 sts, ssk, yo, k2tog, k2. 20 sts.

K 1 row.

K2, ssk, k to last 4 sts, k2tog, k2. 18 sts.

BO all sts.

Back

Left Back

Using size 6 needles, CO 18 sts.

K 4 rows.

Switch to size 7 needles and knit 1 row, purl 1 row.

Break yarn and sl sts to a holder.

Right Back

Repeat as for left back but do not break yarn.

Knit across right back and across sts from holder. 36 sts.

Work 11 rows straight in st st, ending on WS row.

Create opening for tail

K12, BO 12, k12.

P12, CO 12, p12. 36 sts.

Work in st st until the back is the same length as the front where the shaping begins, ending on WS row.

K2, ssk, k to last 4 sts, k2tog, k2. 34 sts.

K2, p2tog, p to last 4 sts, p2tog tbl, k2. 32 sts.

Repeat these two rows 5 times more. 12 sts.

Switch to size 6 needle and k6, sl rem 6 sts to holder.

K back and forth on 6 sts for 4 inches.

BO all sts. Repeat for second strap.

Pocket

Using size 6 needles, CO 14 sts. K 4 rows.

Switch to size 7 needles. K 1 row. K2, p10, k2.

Repeat these two rows twice more.

Switch to size 6 needles and k 4 rows. BO all sts.

Finishing

Lightly block all pieces.

Sew pocket onto front of coveralls.

Sew side seams using mattress stitch.

May Platypus

To make Freddie's Sister May, follow all instructions as for Freddie Platypus, making her dress instead of the coveralls as follows:

Yarn

Brown Sheep Co. Serendipity Tweed, African Violet, 1 skein

Needles

Size US 7 double-pointed needles

Size US 7 circular needles, 16"

Notions

20" of 1/4" satin ribbon for May's dress

Pattern

Using African Violet and dpns, CO 60 sts.

Place marker and join for working in the round, being careful not to twist sts.

K 1 rnd. P 1 rnd. K 3 rnds.

* K2, yo * repeat across rnd. 90 sts.

Switch to circular needles and K 3 rnds.

K12, p20, k25, p20, k13.

K 1 rnd.

K12, BO 20, k25, BO 20, k13.

K12, CO 7, k25, CO 7, k13. 64 sts.

K 3 rnds.

* K2, yo * repeat across rnd. 96 sts.

Knit for 4.5 inches straight.

K 1 rnd. P 1 rnd.

BO all sts.

Finishing

Weave in ends and block lightly.

Thread ribbon through eyelets and tie in a bow, securing ribbon carefully at sides to prevent choking hazard.

Freddie's Coveralls

Size

6 months (12 months, 24 months, 36 months)

Shown in size 24 months

Yarn

Brown Sheep Serendipity Tweed, 60% cotton, 40% wool, 210 yards per 100 grams

Needed for Coveralls

Colorado Columbine, 2 (2, 2, 3) skeins

Needed for Hammer

Poinsettia, 50 yards

Yellow Buttercup, 50 yards

Needles

Size US 5, 6 and 7 circular needles (24"-32") or straight needles

Size US 4 double pointed needles

Gauge

20 sts over 4 inches in stockinette stitch on size US 7 needles

Notions

Stitch holders

Three 7/8" buttons

Two 3/4" circles of wool felt

Two 1" circles of wool felt

Toy stuffing of your choice-- polyfill, roving, or a blend is fine

Pattern Notes

These fun coveralls are trimmed with a simple garter stitch border. Knit flat in two pieces and seamed up the sides, they include a pocket and a hammer loop to carry a knitted toy hammer. The hammer is knit in the round and adds a whimsical touch to a classic and durable knit all children will enjoy.

Pattern

Front

Right side front

Using Colorado Columbine and size 6 needles, CO 37 [39, 40, 42] sts. Knit 6 rows.

Switch to size 7 needles and work in st st for 2.5 [3, 3.5, 4] inches more, ending on WS row.

Break yarn, sl sts to a holder.

Left side front

Repeat as for right front, except do not break yarn.

Continue as follows:

Knit across 34 [36, 37, 39] sts, k2tog, k1, pm, and begin working right side; k1, ssk, knit to end. 72 [76, 78, 82] sts.

Next row: purl

Begin shaping leg join as follows:

Row 1: k to 3 sts before marker, k2tog, k1, sm, k1, ssk, knit to end.

Row 2: purl. 70 [74, 76, 80] sts.

Repeat these two rows 6 times more. 58 [62, 64, 68] sts.

Work st st for 4 [4.5, 5, 6] inches, ending WS row, removing marker.

Front Bib Shaping

Row 1: k3, ssk, knit to last 5 sts, k2tog, k3.

Row 2: k3, purl to last 3 sts, k3. 56 [60, 62, 66] sts.

Repeat these two rows 12 times more. 32 [36, 38, 42] sts.

Make buttonholes as follows:

K3, BO2, k to last 5 sts, BO2, k3.

Next row: k3, CO2, p to last 5 sts, CO2, k3.

Create garter edge trim:

Switch to size 6 needles:

Row 1: k3, ssk, k to last 5 sts, k2tog, k3.

Row 2: knit. 30 [34, 36, 40] sts.

Repeat these two rows twice more. 26 [30, 32, 36] sts.

BO all sts.

Back

Work the back of the coveralls the same as for the front, ending at the Front Bib Shaping.

Continue as follows for back:

Row 1: k3, ssk, k to last 5 sts, k2tog, k3.

Row 2: k3, p2tog, p to last 5 sts, p2tog tbl, k3. 54 [58, 60, 64] sts.

Repeat these 2 rows 8 times more. 22 [26, 28, 32] sts.

Next row: k3, ssk, k to last 5 sts, k2tog, k3.

Next row: k3, purl to last 3 sts, k3. 20 [24, 26, 30] sts.

Repeat these 2 rows 1 [1, 2, 2] times more. 18 [22, 22, 26] sts.

Next row: knit.

Next row: k3, p to last 3 sts, k3.

Repeat these 2 rows 0 [0, 1, 1] time more.

Shape top back:

Row 1: k1, ssk, k to last 3 sts, k2tog, k1.

Row 2: p1, p2tog, p to last 3 sts, p2tog tbl, p1. 14 [18, 18, 22] sts.

Repeat these two rows 2 [3, 3, 4] times more. 6 sts.

K1, ssk, k2tog, k1. 4 sts.

P2tog, p2tog tbl. 2 sts.

K2tog. BO last st.

Straps

Using size 6 needle, pick up and knit 9 sts along angled tip of back left side as shown in photo. Work in garter stitch (knit every row) for 7 [8, 9, 10] inches.

BO all sts.

Repeat for right side.

Hammer Loop

Using size 6 needle, CO 28 sts.

Knit 6 rows. BO all sts.

Pocket

Using size 5 needles, CO 30 sts. K 5 rows.

Switch to size 6 needles and k3, p24, k3. K 1 row.

Repeat these 2 rows for 2.5 inches.

Switch to size 5 needles and k 4 rows. BO all sts.

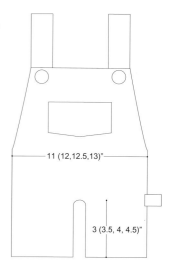

11 (12,12.5,13)"

3 (3.5, 4, 4.5)"

Finishing

Lightly block all pieces.

Sew right side seam using mattress stitch.

Fold hammer loop in half, and sew into left side seam as shown in diagram. Sew left side seam using mattress stitch.

Sew buttons to ends of straps.

Sew button to strap junction on back.

Sew pocket to front of coveralls, placing as shown in photos.

Hammer

Handle

Using Yellow Buttercup and size 4 dpns, using long tail cast-on and leaving a 12" tail, CO 9 sts and divide evenly onto three needles. PM and join for working in the round, being careful not to twist the stitches.

Knit 1 round.

* K1, kfb, k1 * repeat across round. 12 st.

* K1, kfb, k2 * repeat across round. 15 sts.

Purl 1 round.

Knit 5 rounds.

Using CO tail and a yarn needle, cinch together CO stitches to close the center of the circle, and draw thread into center of knitting. Thread 2 3/4" felt circles onto yarn needle, and secure at the inside base of the circle with a double knot.

Knit every round until handle measures 5" from purl row.

BO all sts, leaving a 15" tail.

Head

Using Poinsettia and size 4 dpns, using long tail cast-on and leaving a 12" tail, CO 9 sts and divide evenly onto three needles. PM and join for working in the round, being careful not to twist the stitches.

Knit 1 round.

* K1, kfb, k1 * repeat across round. 12 st.

* K1, kfb, k2 * repeat across round. 15 sts.

* K2, kfb, k2 * repeat across round. 18 sts.

* K2, kfb, k3 * repeat across round. 21 sts.

Purl 1 round.

Knit 6 rounds.

Using CO tail and a yarn needle, cinch together CO stitches to close the center of the circle, and draw thread into center of knitting. Thread two 1" felt circles onto yarn needle, and secure at the inside base of the circle with a double knot.

Knit 7 rounds.

* K2, p1 * repeat across round.

Repeat this round 2 times more.

* K2tog, p1 * repeat across round. 14 sts.

* K1, p1 * repeat for 4 rounds.

* Kfb, p1 * repeat across round. 21 sts.

Knit 2 rounds.
K2tog, knit to end of round. 20 sts.

Place top half of sts onto one dpn, and the bottom half of the sts onto a second dpn. Lightly block hammer handle and head.

Stuff head with fiberfill or roving, and finish edge with 3-needle bind-off. Weave in ends.

Stuff handle, and using tail, sew head to handle as shown in photos. Weave in ends.

Baby Envelope

Size

To fit infant up to 16 pounds

Yarn

Brown Sheep Serendipity Tweed, 60% cotton, 40% wool, 210 yards per 100 grams

Baby's Breath, 4 skeins

Needles

Size US 7 circular needles, 24" or longer

Gauge

20 stitches over 4 inches in garter stitch on size US 7 needles

Pattern Notes

This sweet infant wrap is the perfect all-season blanket for that special little baby you love! I designed it with one side flap longer than the other so it can be wrapped over and back underneath the baby to keep the ends secure. The cotton/wool yarn worked in garter stitch is just perfect for keeping baby warm while allowing for air circulation and comfort for the sweet little one.

Pattern

CO 36 stitches

Shape lower flap:

Row 1 (rs): sl 1 pw wyif, k1, kfb, knit to last 4 sts, kfb, k3. 38 sts.

Rows 2, 3, 4: sl 1 pw wyif, knit to the end of the row.

Repeat these 4 rows 10 times more. 58 sts.

Work straight for bottom flap:

Sl 1 pw wyif, knit to end of row.

Repeat this row until the blanket measures 14 inches from the cast on edge, ending with a wrong side row.

Shape middle panel:

Row 1 (rs): sl1 pw wyif, k1, kfb, knit to last 4 sts, kfb, k3.

Row 2 (ws): sl 1 pw wyif, knit to end of row. 60 sts.

Repeat these 2 rows 24 times more. 108 sts.

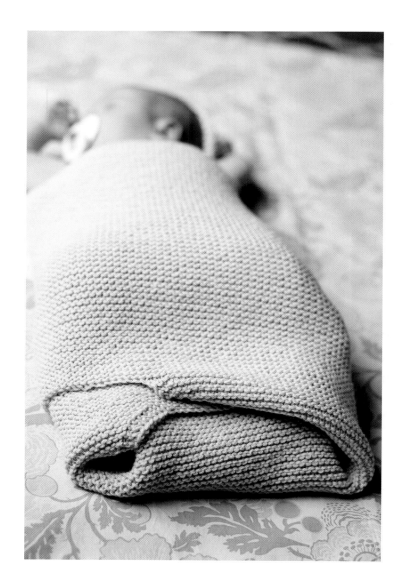

Increase by casting on for side flaps:

Sl 1 pw wyif, knit across row, then, using backward loop cast-on, CO 22 sts. 130 sts.

Next row: knit across row, then, using backward loop cast-on, CO 60 sts. 190 sts.

Shape corners:

Right side row: k2, kfb, knit to last 4 sts, kfb, k3. 192 sts.

Wrong side row: sl 1 pw wyif, knit to end of row.

Row 1 (rs): sl 1 pw wyif, k1, kfb, k to last 4 sts, kfb, k3.

Row 2 (ws): sl 1 pw wyif, k to end. 194 sts.

Repeat these 2 rows once more. 196 sts.

Work straight for middle panel:

Sl 1 pw wyif, knit to end of row.

Repeat this row, working without shaping, for 12 inches, ending on a wrong side row.

Shape corners:

Row 1 (rs): sl 1 pw wyif, k1, ssk, knit to last 4 sts, k2tog, k2.

Row 2 (ws): sl 1 pw wyif, knit to end of row. 194 sts.

Repeat these 2 rows twice more. 190 sts.

Decrease by binding off for side flaps:

Next row (rs): BO 70 sts, knit to the end of the row. 120 sts.

Next row (ws): BO 30 sts, knit to the end of the row. 90 sts.

Shape top panel:

Row 1 (rs): sl1 pw wyif, k1, ssk, knit to last 4 sts, k2tog, k2.

Row 2 (ws): sl1 pw wyif, knit to end of row. 88 sts.

Repeat these two rows 18 times more. 52 sts.

Sl 1 pw wyif, knit to end of row.

Repeat this row 9 times more.

Row 1 (rs): sl 1 pw wyif, k1, ssk, knit to last 4 sts, k2tog, k2.

Row 2 (ws): sl 1 pw wyif, knit to end of row. 50 sts.

Repeat these two rows 8 times more. 34 sts remain.

Last row: sl 1 pw wyif, knit to end of row.

Note: the right side of the blanket is the "inside"- so when you finish the hood it should be done so that the cup of the hood is open toward you while looking at the right side of the blanket.

Divide remaining stitches evenly onto two needles, and finish the top of the hood panel with kitchener stitch or three needle bind-off.

Finishing

Weave in ends and block lightly .

Joanna Johnson has a B.A. in Literature from Drew University and has enjoyed combining her love of books and knitting in this special knitting picture book. She lives in Loveland, Colorado, with her husband, Eric, and their three children, who are a constant source of inspiration for her stories. This is her second book.

Eric Johnson has a B.F.A. from Kutztown University in Graphic Design. After working in commercial design for two decades as a signwriter, muralist, and graphic designer, he has enjoyed returning to his childhood love of drawing by setting pencil to paper to illustrate this book. He lives with his wife, Joanna, and their three children in Loveland, Colorado. This is his second book.

Yarn
Brown Sheep Co, Inc.
100662 CR 16
Mitchell, NE 69357
phone 800.826.9136
brownsheep.com

Deepest thanks to: Our family, friends, and readers, for their encouragement and love. Peggy Jo Wells and the entire staff at Brown Sheep Company for offering yarn support, and, more importantly, friendship and guidance. Amy Butler, for offering fabric support for photo shoots and for our animal fashions. Christa Tippmann, for capturing both the knits and the wonder of childhood so beautifully. Hadley Austin, for being a great tech editor. Megan Helzer, our editorial assistant, for her keen eye. Ann Young, for taking the time to mentor a new knitwear designer and for loaning us beautiful Australian nature and knitting books. Bob O'Brien, for offering his expertise in the subject area of Australia's amazing animals and plants. Melynda Bernardi of French Press Knits for allowing us to borrow her slipper design for the illustrations. Unkin Chris for late night company in the studio. Our models: Parker Dinsmore, Grant and Sam Johnson, and Erin and Pearl McLaughlin, for doing such a great job. Test knitters, for their valuable advice: Amanda Abuhl, for her friendship; Kristin Basset, for connecting over a distance; Jennifer Blythin, for her speed; Megan Helzer, for her faithfulness; Mari Liestman, for her courage; Evangeline Snyder, for her support; and Monika Vargas, for all the advice. We thank our three children for their creativity and their love. We thank God for leading, inspiring, and loving us.

Fabric
Amy Butler Desig
122 S. Prospect St.
Granville, OH 430
phone 740.587.284
amybutlerdesign.co